Eleven Plus
Secondary School Selection

Verbal Reasoning

Additional Practice Questions
Standard <u>and</u> multiple choice
Dual Format

C

Introduction

This book is designed to complement the IPS set of verbal reasoning practice papers. It contains extra questions of all of the types covered in the IPS range.

These are not timed papers, just sheets of extra questions. It provides useful extra practice, especially if there are certain types of questions that the child has difficulty with.

There are many ways to use this book. You could work through the book page by page, but probably a more useful exercise would be to work on two or three questions from a page and then move on. It is up to you to do what you think will benefit your child in preparation for their exam. However you use this book don't try to do too much at any one time and do not try to make it just a series of boring exercises.

If you are still unsure of how the questions work then you can purchase our book on Method and Technique. This covers ALL the question types used in the IPS range. Details can be found on the back cover.

Good luck.

11+ Team

This book comes in <u>Dual Format</u>. This means that it can be used in either multiple choice OR standard format. We are introducing the dual format range in order that you can buy with confidence knowing that the format used in your area will be supported.

Type A.

In each question below, find the **one** letter that will complete the word in front of the brackets and begin the word after the brackets. **The same letter must fit into both sets of brackets.** Mark this letter in the space provided or use the multiple choice answer sheet.

Example.   BLAS   (<u>T</u>)   REASON   SHOR   (<u>T</u>)   RIP

1.   TUR (   ) UND   CLE (   ) ORGE

2.   FEA (   ) RAIL   SQUA (   ) RUST

3.   TAN (   ) NEAD   SLIC (   ) ITTEN

4.   GRI (   ) OISY   CHI (   ) EVER

5.   TRA (   ) ART   WAS (   ) OUND

6.   HEL (   ) EAL   SPREA (   ) RAKE

7.   SCA (   ) EAT   SLI (   ) IND

8.   BLIN (   ) ILO   PRAN (   ) ING

9.   SOF (   ) WAY   COMM (   ) ISLE

10.   BEE (   ) OON   KIS (   ) OLAR

11.   CLA (   ) AND   STRA (   ) EAR

12.   CHAI (   ) IGHT   LIVE (   ) EACH

Type B.

In each question below, find the **two** words that are **different** from the other three and underline them, or mark them on the multiple choice answer sheet.

Example.   Monday   Tuesday   Friday   _month_   _noon_

1.   rubbish   waste   waist   decline   refuse

2.   engross   expand   exist   increase   enlarge

3.   bump   twist   collide   hit   jump

4.   alter   priest   church   modify   change

5.   uncertain   unwell   unusual   uncommon   rare

6.   artistic   musical   cunning   sly   artful

7.   cry   tears   weep   sob   sniff

8.   width   diameter   height   weight   breadth

9.   pencil   paper   sheet   blanket   duvet

10.   telephone   microscope   glasses   radio   telescope

11.   socks   shoes   slippers   tights   boots

12.   aluminium   steal   iron   take   thieve

Type C.

A B C D E F G H I J K L M N O P Q R S T U V W X Y Z

The alphabet has been written above to help you answer the following questions.

In each question below a word is shown in code. The first code word in each question has been worked out for you. Work out the second word/code in the question in the same way and write it in the space provided or mark it on the multiple choice answer sheet.

Example.	If the code for TRAP is USBQ		
	what does DPME mean?	(<u>COLD</u>	)

1. If the code for CHILD is ELOTN
   what does FMBMB mean? (_____)

2. If the code for LETTER is JBRQCO
   what is the code for NUMBER? (_____)

3. If the code for ANNOYED is BQSVHPQ
   what does FAFTYWR mean? (_____)

4. If the code for TABLES is UDGSND
   what is the code for CHAIRS? (_____)

5. If QPUFT means STAND
   what does BWHUU mean? (_____)

6. If the code for PARCEL is QDSFFO
   what is the code for LETTER? (_____)

7. If the code for LEARN is NCCPP
   what does EJKKD mean? (_____)

8. If the code for ENDING is JTIOSM
   what is the code for FINISH? (_____)

9. If the code for SHAVE is RFXRZ
   what does SFBNZ mean? (_____)

10. If the code for CHEAT is BJBEO
    what is the code for SPINE? (_____)

11. If YJPOGS means WINNER
    what does LVOQGS mean? (_____)

12. If the code for HELPED is JDNOGC
    what is the code for GROUND? (_____)

Type D.

In each question below, find two words, **one** from each group, that are the **closest in meaning**. **Underline** these **two** words on the sheet or mark them on the multiple choice answer sheet.

Example.   (*sleep*   run   walk)   (smile   laugh   *snooze*)

1.   (case   work   brief)   (long   tall   short)

2.   (disperse   disappear   disloyal)   (scatter   skater   grapple)

3.   (internet   interior   invention)   (computer   inside   ventilate)

4.   (breathe   puff   loathe)   (hate   cough   chuckle)

5.   (odour   outdoors   peculiar)   (smell   perhaps   country)

6.   (nocturnal   price   penetrate)   (evening   pierce   pushed)

7.   (prohibited   allow   enhanced)   (entrap   forgot   forbidden)

8.   (recluse   reveal   reluctant)   (unwilling   opening   opposite)

9.   (doubtful   deliberately   decided)   (response   tragically   purposely)

10.   (eventually   usually   finished)   (ending   finally   beginning)

11.   (clearing   abnormal   ordinarily)   (normally   finally   moment)

12.   (adhere   abrupt   adopt)   (slide   sudden   buy)

Type E.

In these sentences, a word of four letters is hidden at the end of one word and the beginning of the next word. Find the pair of words that contain the hidden word and underline them on the sheet, writing the word made in the space provided. If you are using the multiple choice answer sheet put a mark by the pair of words which hide the new word.

Example.	The pro<u>be str</u>eaked through outer space	(**best**)

1.   Our class studied electric eels today.   (_____)

2.   Don't send enormous items by post.   (_____)

3.   The sergeant ripped his black coat.   (_____)

4.   Forest fires ignite during the summer.   (_____)

5.   Santa Claus always eats mince pies.   (_____)

6.   Hurry, we can't miss our train.   (_____)

7.   Chocolate has a lovely cocoa taste.   (_____)

8.   Reverend Jones knows the local farmers.   (_____)

9.   Paste poured from the glue pot.   (_____)

10.   Janet decided to plan everything today.   (_____)

11.   Jessica came home at eleven o'clock.   (_____)

12.   Both atlases had many colourful maps .   (_____)

Type F.

In each sentence below, one word, which is in capitals, has had **three consecutive**
out. These **three** letters will make one correctly spelt word without changing the order. Write the
three-letter word in the space provided, or choose the appropriate answer on the multiple choice
answer sheet.

Example.   John bought a new **COMER**.   (*PUT*)   COM___

1.   I walk to school **WHVER** the weather.   (_____)

2.   Harriet wanted to bake **AHER** cake.   (_____)

3.   The **SHOW** end of the pool is the safest.   (_____)

4.   An octopus has many **TACLES**.   (_____)

5.   I had to **SP** to pick up my pen.   (_____)

6.   The **FRILY** horse like being brushed.   (_____)

7.   Grandma collected her **SION** from the post office.   (_____)

8.   The choir sang beautifully in perfect **HONY**   (_____)

9.   I didn't know **SE** books they were, Miss.   (_____)

10.   The gems were taken by **THIS**.   (_____)

11.   Wendy has to **WPER** in the library.   (_____)

12.   **OGES** contain lots of vitamin C.   (_____)

Type G.

In each question below, letters stand for numbers.
Work out the answer to the sum and mark its **letter** in the space provided, or on the multiple choice sheet.

Example.   If A = 2, B = 3, C = 4, D = 5, E = 1, what is the answer to the sum:

$$A + B - E = (C)$$

1.   If A = 8, B = 12, C = 16, D = 4, E = 20, what is the answer to the sum:

$$C \div D + B = (\underline{\quad})$$

2.   If A = 10, B = 11, C = 7, D = 4, E = 2, what is the answer to the sum:

$$E \times B - C - D = (\underline{\quad})$$

3.   If A = 5, B = 10, C = 2, D = 20, E = 17, what is the answer to the sum:

$$A \times C + B = (\underline{\quad})$$

4.   If A =100, B = 50, C = 20, D = 10, E = 120, what is the answer to the sum:

$$D \times C - B - A = (\underline{\quad})$$

5.   If A = 2, B = 6, C = 18, D = 24, E = 12, what is the answer to the sum:

$$A \times E + B - C = (\underline{\quad})$$

6.   If A = 2, B = 4, C = 24, D = 16, E = 3, what is the answer to the sum:

$$B \times E \times A = (\underline{\quad})$$

<u>Type G (Continued).</u>

7. If A = 4, B = 2, C = 0, D = 3, E = 7, what is the answer to the sum:

$$B \times C \times B + D = (\underline{\quad})$$

8. If A = 20, B = 4, C = 16, D = 12, E = 5, what is the answer to the sum:

$$A \div B \times E - E = (\underline{\quad})$$

9. If A = 24, B = 8, C = 20, D = 16, E = 4, what is the answer to the sum:

$$C - E + B - C = (\underline{\quad})$$

10. If A = 2, B = 3, C = 16, D = 14, E = 7, what is the answer to the sum:

$$D \div A \times B - E = (\underline{\quad})$$

11. If A = 75, B = 5, C = 10, D = 50, E = 150, what is the answer to the sum:

$$E \div D \times B - B = (\underline{\quad})$$

12. If A = 12, B = 8, C = 16, D = 4, E = 3, what is the answer to the sum:

$$D \times B - D - C = (\underline{\quad})$$

Type H.

In each question below, find **two** words, **one** from each group, that are the **most opposite in meaning**.

Underline these **two** words on the sheet below, or mark the two words on the multiple choice answer sheet.

Example.	(*up* run walk)	(smile laugh *down*)
1.	(few minority many)	(mostly certainly majority)
2.	(frightened legion failure)	(sanitary success strength)
3.	(foolish ignoramus rude)	(wise known silent)
4.	(advance adhere admit)	(retreat retry repeat)
5.	(abandon attract arrival)	(visit departure retire)
6.	(fib bold blame)	(glib timid tiresome)
7.	(contact contain conceal)	(repeal freed reveal)
8.	(dredge danger dagger)	(safely safety knife)
9.	(applause enough tranquil)	(rough smooth trough)
10.	(innocent creep change)	(guilty blank charge)
11.	(influence permit credit)	(collect forbid payment)
12.	(beautiful scared plentiful)	(fright graceful scarce)

Type I.

In each question, find the number that will complete the sum correctly and mark it in the space provided or mark the appropriate box on the multiple choice answer sheet.

Example. $25 + 17 - 3 = 12 \times 3 + (\underline{3})$

1. $53 - 9 - 7 = 6 \times 3 + (\underline{})$

2. $90 \div 15 + 8 = 28 \div 4 + (\underline{})$

3. $3 \times 4 \times 5 = 2 \times 3 \times (\underline{})$

4. $16 \div 4 \times 8 = 5 \times 9 - (\underline{})$

5. $150 \div 3 + 6 = 8 \times 3 + (\underline{})$

6. $19 + 35 + 17 = 5 \times 9 + (\underline{})$

7. $54 \div 6 \times 12 = 9 \times 2 \times (\underline{})$

8. $48 \div 16 \times 8 = 12 \times 3 - (\underline{})$

9. $115 - 30 - 25 = 20 + 17 + (\underline{})$

10. $85 \div 5 + 4 = 30 \div 2 + (\underline{})$

11. $49 + 17 + 15 = 9 \times 9 + (\underline{})$

12. $30 - 11 - 6 = 50 - 21 - (\underline{})$

Type J.

In each question below, **one** letter from the word on the left must be moved into the word on the right to make **two** new words. The letters must not be re-arranged. **Both** new words must make sense. Write the two new words in the spaces provided, or mark the correct letter on the multiple choice answer sheet.

Example.	CLIMB	LOSE	(C)	LIMB	CLOSE

1.	TIRED	SPIES	_____	_____

2.	PLACE	BOND	_____	_____

3.	BRAIN	FIRE	_____	_____

4.	GRIND	BEAN	_____	_____

5.	BLEND	CAMP	_____	_____

6.	CREAM	CHAT	_____	_____

7.	BRAND	MEAL	_____	_____

8.	EVENT	LIRE	_____	_____

9.	FARCE	PATH	_____	_____

10.	WRING	SELL	_____	_____

11.	TRAMP	RELY	_____	_____

12.	SCENT	PURE	_____	_____

Type K.

In these questions the numbers in each group are related in the same way. You must find the missing number in the third group and write it in the space provided or on the multiple choice answer sheet.

Example.   (5 [15] 10)   (8 [17] 9)   (10 [*30*] 20)

1.   (17 [23] 40)   (19 [32] 51)   (12 [___] 48)

2.   (7 [19] 5)   (6 [24] 12)   (10 [___] 11)

3.   (4 [30] 7)   (5 [37] 7)   (6 [___] 8)

4.   (9 [18] 4)   (5 [20] 8)   (8 [___] 8)

5.   (25 [24] 49)   (29 [33] 62)   (36 [___] 72)

6.   (25 [12] 12)   (32 [22] 9)   (35 [___] 14)

7.   (17 [66] 50)   (20 [48] 44)   (35 [___] 60)

8.   (6 [8] 36)   (7 [9] 49)   (8 [___] 56)

9.   (2 [40] 10)   (5 [90] 9)   (6 [___] 6)

10.   (6 [20] 11)   (7 [16] 6)   (9 [___] 13)

11.   (16 [23] 30)   (19 [26] 33)   (26 [___] 42)

12.   (7 [32] 9)   (12 [42] 9)   (18 [___] 9)

Type L.

A B C D E F G H I J K L M N O P Q R S T U V W X Y Z

The alphabet has been written above to help you answer the following questions.

Find the pair of letters that continue each series in the most sensible way. Write the answer in the space provided, or mark the appropriate box on the multiple choice answer sheet.

Example.   AB,   BC,   CD,   DE,   EF,   (*FG*)

1.   GY,   JX,   MW,   PV,   SU,   (_____)

2.   HL,   JN,   LP,   NR,   PT,   (_____)

3.   HP,   IO,   KM   NJ,   RF ,   (_____)

4.   GW,   DZ,   AC,   XF,   UI,   (_____)

5.   AB,   ZY,   CD,   XW,   EF,   (_____)

6.   VF,   WD,   XB,   YZ,   ZX,   (_____)

7.   TX,   VV,   XT,   ZR,   BP,   (_____)

8.   SY,   TW,   VU,   YS,   CQ,   (_____)

9.   FG,   CI,   ZK,   WM,   TO ,   (_____)

10.   AZ,   ZA,   XC,   UF,   QJ,   (_____)

11.   RG,   QI,   PK,   OM,   NO,   (_____)

12.   JP,   HR,   FT,   DV,   BX,   (_____)

Type M.

In these questions find the <u>two</u> words, <u>one</u> from each group that will complete the sentence in the best way. Underline **BOTH** words on the answer sheet below, or mark both words on the multiple choice answer sheet.

Example.   Time is to (first, <u>second</u>. third)
                as distance is to (gram, kilo, <u>metre</u>).   (**second, metre**)

1.   Dial is to (ring, laid, phone)
          as madam is to (lady, woman, madam).

2.   Dozen is to (twenty, fifteen, twelve)
          as score is to (hit, run, twenty).

3.   Slide is to (slip, swing, chute)
          as fall is to (water, collapse, jump).

4.   Goat is to (child, kid, nanny)
          as elephant is to (calf, cub, trunk).

5.   Chuckle is to (brother, throw, laugh)
          as weep is to (clean, tidy, cry).

6.   tricycle is to (child, young, three)
          as bicycle is to (saddle, two, ride).

7.   March is to (June, November. February)
          as November is to (October, December, January,).

8.   Angle is to (heaven, degrees, wings)
          as water is to (wine, jug, litres).

9.   Butter is to (margarine, cup, milk)
          as wine is to (bottle, grapes, squash).

10.   Butcher is to (shop, meat, knife)
          as greengrocer is to (plant, market, vegetables).

11.   Car is to (driver, garage, van)
          as aeroplane is to (sky, hangar, wings).

12.   Eye is to (glasses, sight, blind)
          as nose is to (sniff, nostril, smell).

Type N.

Three of these four words are given in code.
The codes are not written in the same order as the words and one code is missing.

For these questions mark the answers in the spaces provided, or choose the appropriate answer on the multiple choice answer sheet.

BEND   DONE   LEAD   DEAF
8346   1648   7628

1.   Find the code for the word **BANNED**   (_____)

2.   Find the code for the word **NEEDLE**   (_____)

3.   Find the word for the code **6421768**   (_____)

****

SALE   MEAL   LAST   TEAM
4928   1259   5214

4.   Find the code for the word **METAL**   (_____)

5.   Find the code for the word **SLATE**   (_____)

6.   Find the word for the code **18255914**   (_____)

****

JUST   ROTS   STAG   LATE
6389   5834   1258

7.   Find the code for the word **JUGGLE**   (_____)

8.   Find the code for the word **GUESTS**   (_____)

9.   Find the word for the code **83589**   (_____)

Type N (continued).

CAKE   LARK   LUCK   CLUE

9825   9635   6812

10.   Find the code for the word **CRACKLE**   (_____)

11.   Find the code for the word **RECALL**   (_____)

12.   Find the word for the code **96581**   (_____)

****

PALM   LAST   ROSE   MEAT

1458   8647   5437

13.   Find the code for the word **METAL**   (_____)

14.   Find the code for the word **TEAMS**   (_____)

15.   Find the word for the code **374156**   (_____)

****

NICE   ENDS   NEAT   DIVE

3154   7194   4736

16.   Find the code for the word **SCIENCE**   (_____)

17.   Find the code for the word **SIDES**   (_____)

18.   Find the word for the code **345194**   (_____)

Type O.

In these questions there are three pairs of words. You must complete the third pair in the same way as the first two pairs. Write the new word in the space provided, or select an answer on the multiple choice answer sheet.

Example.   (grind, grin) (fore, for)
                                    (piper, _pipe_)

1.   (ladder, dead) (garden, read)
                                    (factor, _____)

2.   (target, gate) (roared, rode)
                                    (soften, _____)

3.   (either, tier) (donate, node)
                                    (dawdle, _____)

4.   (trimmer, timer) (planner, panel)
                                    (terrace, _____)

5.   (letters, rest) (gutters, rust)
                                    (baskets, _____)

6.   (future, turf) (thrift, rift)
                                    (define, _____)

7.   (tissue, issues) (bridge, ridges)
                                    (stable, _____)

8.   (banana, nan) (career, err)
                                    (settle, _____)

9.   (repeat, tape) (valley, yell)
                                    (spiral, _____)

10.   (draw, ward) (part, trap)
                                    (rats, _____)

11.   (rights, sight) (balls, call)
                                    (lights, _____)

12.   (decide, dice) (breeze, beer)
                                    (stroke, _____)

Type P.

In these questions you need to find the number that should appear in the brackets and continues the series in the most sensible way. Write this number in the space provided, or choose the appropriate answer from the multiple choice answer sheet.

Example.   5,   10,   15,   20,   25,   (_30_)

1.   19,   21,   25,   31,   39,   (_____)

2.   17,   23,   27,   33,   37,   (_____)

3.   17,   18,   20,   23,   27,   (_____)

4.   35,   32,   30,   27,   25,   (_____)

5.   27,   28,   24,   25,   21,   (_____)

6.   160,   80,   40,   20,   10,   (_____)

7.   17,   16,   14,   13,   11,   (_____)

8.   3,   6,   8,   16,   18,   36,   (_____)

9.   15,   14,   16,   13,   17,   12,   (_____)

10.   62,   60,   30,   28,   14,   (_____)

11.   1,   1,   2,   6,   24,   (_____)

12.   7,   17,   25,   31,   35,   (_____)

Type Q.

In each question below, Underline the **two** words, **one** from each set, that together make **one** correctly spelt word, without changing the order of the letters. **The word from the set on the left always comes first.**

Alternatively, you can mark the two words on the multiple choice answer sheet

Example.   (*motor*   gas   electric)   (engine   bus   *cycle*)   (**Motorcycle**)

1.   (body   arm   leg)   (your   their   our)

2.   (all   many   none)   (sow   owed   owned)

3.   (stump   stub   bust)   (alive   create   born)

4.   (real   dirt   mess)   (ill   sent   age)

5.   (heat   sun   shine)   (him   her   there)

6.   (swallow   sup   sip)   (up   port   poise)

7.   (be   see   fee)   (shore   view   long)

8.   (half   whole   part)   (many   some   all)

9.   (trod   walked   guard)   (den   hole   in)

10.   (out   on   in)   (peck   sure   time)

11.   (made   occur   blind)   (bring   red   grey)

12.   (pound   dollar   cent)   (rally   race   run)

Type R.

In each question below, the three words in the second group should go together in the same way as the three in the first group. Find the missing word from the second group and write it in the space provided, or find the correct answer on the multiple choice answer sheet.

Example.	lint	[liner]	term
	drop	[*drove*]	even
1.	clamp	[damp]	modem
	blend	[_____]	cuffs
2.	paper	[crane]	chain
	vixen	[_____]	scour
3.	laser	[smile]	moist
	taped	[_____]	learn
4.	tangle	[grain]	print
	better	[_____]	tramp
5.	sharp	[hairs]	shiny
	bless	[_____]	train
6.	blank	[cable]	crate
	enact	[_____]	tired
7.	ocean	[crane]	nerve
	steam	[_____]	derby
8.	clear	[racer]	realm
	retry	[_____]	drive
9.	side	[dust]	tune
	nile	[_____]	each
10.	sheet	[trees]	paper
	deals	[_____]	burnt
11.	beacons	[chase]	short
	precise	[_____]	alarm

Type S.

In each question below, there are two pairs of words. You must find a word from the list that will go equally well with either pair. Write this word in the space provided, or find the correct word on the multiple choice answer sheet.

Example.

OFFICE   CHAIN   BEACH   FARM   STABLE

(STEADY   FIRM)   (BARN   SHED)   (_STABLE_)

1.   *MUSCLE   TIN   ENERGY   MIGHT   MAYBE*

(POWER   STRENGTH)   (MAY   CAN)   (_____)

2.   *NOTICE   LOOK   PROMOTION   POINT   DIRECTION*

(SEE   SPOT)   (ADVERTISEMENT   SIGN)   (_____)

3.   *STREAM   END   DRIP   LOWER   DROP*

(TRICKLE   GLOBULE)   (DECLINE   DECREASE)   (_____)

4.   *NICE   HAPPY   CLUB   KIND   BAND*

(CONSIDERATE   CARING)   (TYPE   GROUP)   (_____)

5.   *HEARTY   WELL   JUMP   TAP   SPRITE*

(HEALTHY   FIT)   (SPRING   WATERHOLE)   (_____)

6.   *FLAP   SIGN   CREASE   WHISPER   SEA*

(WAVE   FLUTTER)   (TAB   FOLD)   (_____)

Type S (Continued).

7.   *VICTORIOUS   SMACKED   SLAPPED   LOST   BEATEN*

           (STRUCK HIT)   (CONQUERED   DEFEATED)   (_____)

8.   *BILL   HURRY   CHARGE   PRICE   HIT*

           (COST   FEE)   (RUSH   ATTACK)   (_____)

9.   *CLING   HOLD   CLAW   CATCH   SPRING*

           (HOOK   LATCH)   (GRAB   GRASP)   (_____)

10.   *STREAK   FANFARE   BAND   CHEVRON   UNDRESS*

           (STRIP   STRIPE)   (GROUP   ORCHESTRA)   (_____)

11.   *PREPARE   CHARGE   DIRECT   RUN   CO-ORDINATE*

           (SPRINT   RUSH)   (MANAGE   ORGANISE)   (_____)

12.   *POINT   AIM   DREAM   ASPIRATION   LOCATION*

           (PINPOINT   TARGET)   (AMBITION   OBJECTIVE)   (_____)

Type U.

A B C D E F G H I J K L M N O P Q R S T U V W X Y Z

The alphabet has been written above to help you answer the following questions.

In each question below, find the letters that will complete the sentence in the best way and mark the correct answer in the space provided, or mark the answer on the multiple choice answer sheet.

Example.   DE is to FG

as ST is to [*UV*]

1.   DE is to GF

as XY is to   [_____]

2.   VU is to UR

as JG is to   [_____]

3.   PJ is to QG

as OB is to   [_____]

4.   XU is to BW

as DT is to   [_____]

5.   BY is to ZA

as CU is to   [_____]

6.   TP is to SO

as MN is to   [_____]

7.   AB is to EF

as GH is to   [_____]

8.   AX is to WB

as PQ is to   [_____]

9.   DT is to ES

as PR is to   [_____]

10.   BF is to DH

as CD is to   [_____]

11.   XY is to WB

as VZ is to   [_____]

12.   QQ is to TP

as DE is to   [_____]

Type Z.

Read the following information, then find the correct answer to the question and write it in the space provided, or mark it on the multiple choice answer sheet.

1.   Mr Green, Mr Brown and Mr Grey all work in a bank.

Mr Brown leaves for work at 7.30 a.m., ten minutes before Mr Green.
Mr Green takes an hour to get to work, 15 minutes less than Mr Grey who leaves home at 7.00 a.m.
Mr Brown arrives at the bank at 8.50 a.m.

At what time does Mr Grey arrive at work?   _____

Read the following information, then find the correct answer to the question and mark it in the box provided on the question sheet, or mark the appropriate box on the multiple choice answer sheet.

2.   Thomas, Dominic and Fiorella all had chips with their lunch. Dominic had a beef burger and Fiorella had two fish fingers. Thomas had a glass of cola, whilst Dominic and Fiorella had a lemon drink each.

If this statement is true, only one of the sentences below is true. Place a cross in the box next to the TRUE statement.

A.	Thomas doesn't like fish fingers.	☐
B.	Dominic had a beef burger, chips and a lemon drink.	☐
C.	Thomas had more chips than Dominic.	☐
D.	Fiorella had fish fingers, chips and a cola.	☐
E.	Thomas and Fiorella shared a lemon drink.	☐

Read the following information, then find the correct answer to the question and write it in the space provided, or mark it on the multiple choice answer sheet.

3.   Catherine, Alison, Darren, Peter and Gillian are collecting pop star stickers.

Darren has twice as many stickers as Alison. Peter has five more than Gillian. Catherine has only one sticker, half as many as Gillian and four less than Alison.

How many stickers does Darren have?   _____

Read the following information, then find the correct answer to the question and write it in the space provided, or mark it on the multiple choice answer sheet.

4.   Philip's dad is four times older than Philip will be next year.

If Philip's dad is 37 next birthday, then how old is Philip?   _____

Type Z.

Read the following information, then find the correct answer to the question and write it in the space provided, or mark it on the multiple choice answer sheet.

5.   Eleanor, Emma, Matthew, Callum and Duncan are travelling down on an escalator in the shopping centre.

Emma is three steps below Eleanor, who is 5 steps below Callum.
Matthew is one step below Callum who is four steps above Duncan.

Who is the <u>second</u> person to step off the escalator?   _____

Read the following information, then find the correct answer to the question and write it in the space provided, or mark it on the multiple choice answer sheet.

6.   If the day before yesterday was Saturday, what day will it be two days after tomorrow?   _____

Read the following information, then find the correct answer to the question and mark it in the spaces provided on the question sheet, or mark the appropriate boxes on the multiple choice answer sheet.

7.   Giles, Bobby, Habib, Melanie and Isabella all belong to the junior athletics team. As part of their training they run laps around the sports centre running track.

Isabella, Habib and Giles run 6 laps on Monday.
Melanie and Isabella run 12 laps on Tuesday.
Giles and Melanie run 9 laps on Wednesday.
Habib, Bobby and Giles run 6 laps on Thursday.
Bobby and Isabella run 6 laps on Friday.
Habib and Melanie run 9 laps on Saturday.

   A.   Which <u>two</u> people run the same number of laps of the track in a week?

                              _____   _____

Read the following information, then find the correct answer to the question and write it in the space provided, or mark it on the multiple choice answer sheet.

8.   It's time for assembly and the teacher, Mrs Bateman, has asked Christopher, Carol, Gemma, Owen and William to line up by the door in order of height, with the tallest at the back of the line.

William is 146 cm tall, shorter than Mrs Bateman but taller than Owen. Carol is taller than Gemma, but shorter than Owen. Christopher is shorter than Owen but is not the shortest of the five.

Which child stands nearest to the door?   _____

Notes

Multiple Choice Answer Sheets

A

Ex.		1.		2.		3.		4.		5.		6.	
C	[ ]	P	[ ]	R	[ ]	E	[ ]	P	[ ]	Y	[ ]	D	[ ]
E	[ ]	F	[ ]	F	[ ]	S	[ ]	F	[ ]	P	[ ]	P	[ ]
D	[ ]	G	[ ]	T	[ ]	B	[ ]	T	[ ]	H	[ ]	M	[ ]
T	[■]	E	[ ]	C	[ ]	M	[ ]	N	[ ]	E	[ ]	T	[ ]
A	[ ]	Y	[ ]	D	[ ]	K	[ ]	W	[ ]	M	[ ]	V	[ ]

7.		8.		9.		10.		11.		12.	
B	[ ]	D	[ ]	S	[ ]	T	[ ]	D	[ ]	B	[ ]
T	[ ]	S	[ ]	T	[ ]	S	[ ]	N	[ ]	G	[ ]
W	[ ]	T	[ ]	A	[ ]	D	[ ]	W	[ ]	N	[ ]
M	[ ]	R	[ ]	R	[ ]	N	[ ]	P	[ ]	M	[ ]
N	[ ]	K	[ ]	W	[ ]	F	[ ]	M	[ ]	R	[ ]

B

Ex.		1.		2.		3.		4.	
Monday	[ ]	rubbish	[ ]	engross	[ ]	bump	[ ]	alter	[ ]
Tuesday	[ ]	waste	[ ]	expand	[ ]	twist	[ ]	priest	[ ]
Friday	[ ]	waist	[ ]	exist	[ ]	collide	[ ]	church	[ ]
month	[■]	decline	[ ]	increase	[ ]	hit	[ ]	modify	[ ]
noon	[■]	refuse	[ ]	enlarge	[ ]	jump	[ ]	change	[ ]

5.		6.		7.		8.		9.	
uncertain	[ ]	artistic	[ ]	cry	[ ]	width	[ ]	pencil	[ ]
unwell	[ ]	musical	[ ]	tears	[ ]	diameter	[ ]	paper	[ ]
unusual	[ ]	cunning	[ ]	weep	[ ]	height	[ ]	sheet	[ ]
uncommon	[ ]	sly	[ ]	sob	[ ]	weight	[ ]	blanket	[ ]
rare	[ ]	artful	[ ]	sniff	[ ]	breadth	[ ]	duvet	[ ]

10.		11.		12.	
telephone	[ ]	socks	[ ]	aluminium	[ ]
microscope	[ ]	shoes	[ ]	steal	[ ]
glasses	[ ]	slippers	[ ]	iron	[ ]
radio	[ ]	tights	[ ]	take	[ ]
telescope	[ ]	boots	[ ]	thieve	[ ]

C

Ex.		1.		2.		3.		4.	
COLT	[ ]	DRIVE	[ ]	LRKYOC	[ ]	EXCERPT	[ ]	DKFODA	[ ]
CLAN	[ ]	DIVER	[ ]	LRKXOC	[ ]	EXHIBIT	[ ]	DJGPAD	[ ]
CAST	[ ]	DINER	[ ]	LRKXCO	[ ]	GRAPPLE	[ ]	DKFPAD	[ ]
COAL	[ ]	DRONE	[ ]	LRKYCO	[ ]	GRIZZLE	[ ]	DFKPAD	[ ]
COLD	[■]	DIVOT	[ ]	LRKYDO	[ ]	EXAMPLE	[ ]	DKFOAD	[ ]

©Internet Primary School Ltd 2003 All copying of this material is prohibited

Multiple Choice Answer Sheets

C

5.

CHASE	[ ]
DUNCE	[ ]
CHANT	[ ]
DANCE	[ ]
ZEBRA	[ ]

6.

KHUWFU	[ ]
MHUWFU	[ ]
MHUFUW	[ ]
KEUWUF	[ ]
KGUWFU	[ ]

7.

CLAMP	[ ]
CRAMP	[ ]
THUMB	[ ]
CLIMB	[ ]
THUMP	[ ]

8.

LNSOXN	[ ]
LOSOXN	[ ]
KOSOXN	[ ]
KOSPXN	[ ]
KOSOYN	[ ]

9.

THERE	[ ]
THREE	[ ]
THYME	[ ]
THEME	[ ]
THEIR	[ ]

10.

RRFRZ	[ ]
RRRFZ	[ ]
TRFRZ	[ ]
TRGRZ	[ ]
RGFRZ	[ ]

11

JASPER	[ ]
JUMBLE	[ ]
JANGLE	[ ]
JUNGLE	[ ]
JUMPER	[ ]

12.

IQPSPC	[ ]
IPQTPC	[ ]
IQQTPC	[ ]
IQQPTC	[ ]
IPQSQC	[ ]

D

Ex.

sleep	[━]	smile	[ ]
run	[ ]	laugh	[ ]
walk	[ ]	snooze	[━]

1.

case	[ ]	long	[ ]
work	[ ]	tall	[ ]
brief	[ ]	short	[ ]

2.

disperse	[ ]	scatter	[ ]
disappear	[ ]	skater	[ ]
disloyal	[ ]	grapple	[ ]

3.

internet	[ ]	computer	[ ]
interior	[ ]	inside	[ ]
invention	[ ]	ventilate	[ ]

4.

breath	[ ]	hate	[ ]
puff	[ ]	cough	[ ]
loathe	[ ]	chuckle	[ ]

5.

odour	[ ]	smell	[ ]
outdoors	[ ]	perhaps	[ ]
peculiar	[ ]	country	[ ]

6.

nocturnal	[ ]	evening	[ ]
price	[ ]	pierce	[ ]
penetrate	[ ]	pushed	[ ]

7.

prohibited	[ ]	entrap	[ ]
allow	[ ]	forgot	[ ]
enhanced	[ ]	forbidden	[ ]

8.

recluse	[ ]	unwilling	[ ]
reveal	[ ]	opening	[ ]
reluctant	[ ]	opposite	[ ]

9.

doubtful	[ ]	response	[ ]
deliberately	[ ]	tragically	[ ]
decided	[ ]	purposely	[ ]

10.

eventually	[ ]	ending	[ ]
usually	[ ]	finally	[ ]
finished	[ ]	beginning	[ ]

11.

clearing	[ ]	normally	[ ]
abnormal	[ ]	finally	[ ]
ordinarily	[ ]	moment	[ ]

12.

adhere	[ ]	slide	[ ]
abrupt	[ ]	sudden	[ ]
adopt	[ ]	buy	[ ]

Multiple Choice Answer Sheets

Ex.

E

The probe	[ ]	through outer	[ ]
probe streaked	[■]	outer space	[ ]
streaked through	[ ]		

1.

Our class	[ ]	electric eels	[ ]
class studied	[ ]	eels today	[ ]
studied electric	[ ]		

2.

Don't send	[ ]	items in	[ ]
send enormous	[ ]	the post	[ ]
enormous items	[ ]		

3.

The sergeant	[ ]	his black	[ ]
sergeant ripped	[ ]	black coat	[ ]
ripped his	[ ]		

4.

Forest fires	[ ]	during the	[ ]
fires ignite	[ ]	the summer	[ ]
ignite during	[ ]		

5.

Santa Claus	[ ]	eats mince	[ ]
Claus always	[ ]	mince pies	[ ]
Always eats	[ ]		

6.

Hurry, we	[ ]	miss our	[ ]
we can't	[ ]	our train	[ ]
can't miss	[ ]		

7.

Chocolate has	[ ]	lovely cocoa	[ ]
has a	[ ]	cocoa taste	[ ]
a lovely	[ ]		

8.

Reverend Jones	[ ]	the local	[ ]
Jones knows	[ ]	local farmers	[ ]
knows the	[ ]		

9.

Paste poured	[ ]	the glue	[ ]
poured from	[ ]	glue pot.	[ ]
from the	[ ]		

10.

Janet decided	[ ]	plan everything	[ ]
decided to	[ ]	everything today	[ ]
to plan	[ ]		

11.

Jessica came	[ ]	at eleven	[ ]
came home	[ ]	eleven o'clock	[ ]
home at	[ ]		

12.

Both atlases	[ ]	many colourful	[ ]
atlases had	[ ]	colourful maps	[ ]
dad many	[ ]		

Ex.

F

pat	[ ]
pet	[ ]
pot	[ ]
put	[■]
pit	[ ]

1.

are	[ ]
tie	[ ]
tee	[ ]
imp	[ ]
ate	[ ]

2.

not	[ ]
far	[ ]
nut	[ ]
pen	[ ]
net	[ ]

3.

and	[ ]
ill	[ ]
end	[ ]
all	[ ]
are	[ ]

4.

too	[ ]
ten	[ ]
tie	[ ]
tea	[ ]
tip	[ ]

5.

and	[ ]
end	[ ]
oil	[ ]
too	[ ]
oat	[ ]

6.

ate	[ ]
not	[ ]
din	[ ]
end	[ ]
nod	[ ]

Multiple Choice Answer Sheets

F

7.
pat	[ ]
pet	[ ]
pot	[ ]
pen	[ ]
pit	[ ]

8.
are	[ ]
arc	[ ]
ear	[ ]
arm	[ ]
all	[ ]

9.
got	[ ]
how	[ ]
one	[ ]
who	[ ]
lid	[ ]

10.
eve	[ ]
pop	[ ]
tin	[ ]
pie	[ ]
pin	[ ]

11.
aim	[ ]
end	[ ]
our	[ ]
her	[ ]
his	[ ]

12.
red	[ ]
ran	[ ]
eel	[ ]
leg	[ ]
hog	[ ]

G

Ex.
A	[ ]
B	[ ]
C	[■]
D	[ ]
E	[ ]

1.
A	[ ]
B	[ ]
C	[ ]
D	[ ]
E	[ ]

2.
A	[ ]
B	[ ]
C	[ ]
D	[ ]
E	[ ]

3.
A	[ ]
B	[ ]
C	[ ]
D	[ ]
E	[ ]

4.
A	[ ]
B	[ ]
C	[ ]
D	[ ]
E	[ ]

5.
A	[ ]
B	[ ]
C	[ ]
D	[ ]
E	[ ]

6.
A	[ ]
B	[ ]
C	[ ]
D	[ ]
E	[ ]

7.
A	[ ]
B	[ ]
C	[ ]
D	[ ]
E	[ ]

8.
A	[ ]
B	[ ]
C	[ ]
D	[ ]
E	[ ]

9.
A	[ ]
B	[ ]
C	[ ]
D	[ ]
E	[ ]

10.
A	[ ]
B	[ ]
C	[ ]
D	[ ]
E	[ ]

11.
A	[ ]
B	[ ]
C	[ ]
D	[ ]
E	[ ]

12.
A	[ ]
B	[ ]
C	[ ]
D	[ ]
E	[ ]

H

Ex.
up	[■]	smile	[ ]
run	[ ]	laugh	[ ]
walk	[ ]	down	[■]

1.
few	[ ]	mostly	[ ]
minority	[ ]	certainly	[ ]
many	[ ]	majority	[ ]

2.
frightened	[ ]	sanitary	[ ]
legion	[ ]	success	[ ]
failure	[ ]	strength	[ ]

3.
foolish	[ ]	wise	[ ]
ignoramus	[ ]	known	[ ]
rude	[ ]	silent	[ ]

4.
advance	[ ]	retreat	[ ]
adhere	[ ]	retry	[ ]
admit	[ ]	repeat	[ ]

5.
abandon	[ ]	visit	[ ]
attract	[ ]	departure	[ ]
arrival	[ ]	retire	[ ]

6.
fib	[ ]	glib	[ ]
bold	[ ]	timid	[ ]
blame	[ ]	tiresome	[ ]

7.
contact	[ ]	repeal	[ ]
contain	[ ]	freed	[ ]
conceal	[ ]	reveal	[ ]

8.
dredge	[ ]	safely	[ ]
danger	[ ]	safety	[ ]
dagger	[ ]	knife	[ ]

9.
applause	[ ]	rough	[ ]
enough	[ ]	smooth	[ ]
tranquil	[ ]	trough	[ ]

10.
innocent	[ ]	guilty	[ ]
creep	[ ]	blank	[ ]
change	[ ]	charge	[ ]

11.
influence	[ ]	collect	[ ]
permit	[ ]	forbid	[ ]
credit	[ ]	payment	[ ]

Multiple Choice Answer Sheets

12.

H

beautiful	[ ]	fright	[ ]
scared	[ ]	graceful	[ ]
plentiful	[ ]	scarce	[ ]

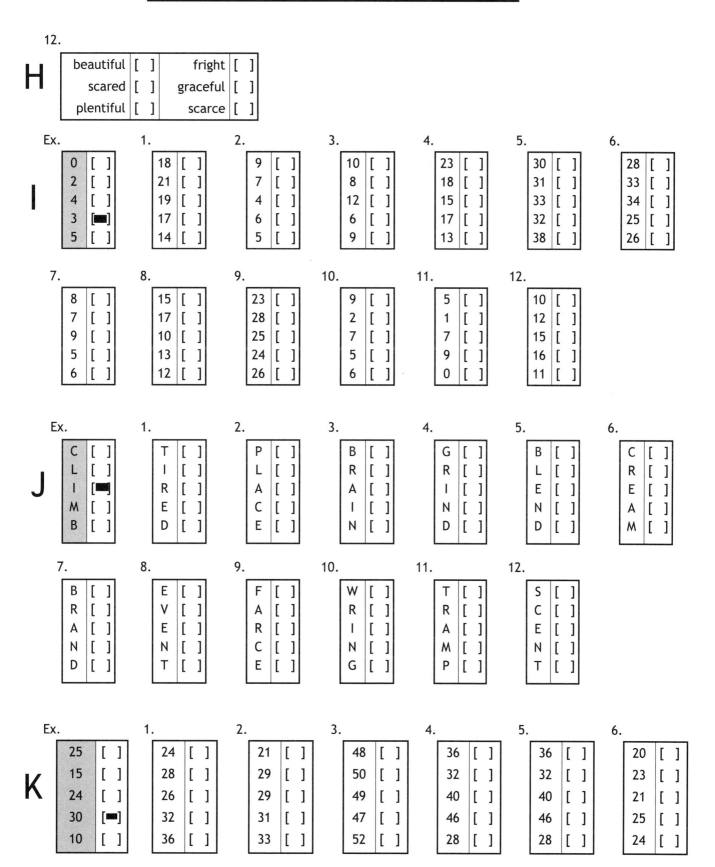

I

Ex.
0	[ ]
2	[ ]
4	[ ]
3	[■]
5	[ ]

1.
18	[ ]
21	[ ]
19	[ ]
17	[ ]
14	[ ]

2.
9	[ ]
7	[ ]
4	[ ]
6	[ ]
5	[ ]

3.
10	[ ]
8	[ ]
12	[ ]
6	[ ]
9	[ ]

4.
23	[ ]
18	[ ]
15	[ ]
17	[ ]
13	[ ]

5.
30	[ ]
31	[ ]
33	[ ]
32	[ ]
38	[ ]

6.
28	[ ]
33	[ ]
34	[ ]
25	[ ]
26	[ ]

7.
8	[ ]
7	[ ]
9	[ ]
5	[ ]
6	[ ]

8.
15	[ ]
17	[ ]
10	[ ]
13	[ ]
12	[ ]

9.
23	[ ]
28	[ ]
25	[ ]
24	[ ]
26	[ ]

10.
9	[ ]
2	[ ]
7	[ ]
5	[ ]
6	[ ]

11.
5	[ ]
1	[ ]
7	[ ]
9	[ ]
0	[ ]

12.
10	[ ]
12	[ ]
15	[ ]
16	[ ]
11	[ ]

J

Ex.
C	[ ]
L	[ ]
I	[■]
M	[ ]
B	[ ]

1.
T	[ ]
I	[ ]
R	[ ]
E	[ ]
D	[ ]

2.
P	[ ]
L	[ ]
A	[ ]
C	[ ]
E	[ ]

3.
B	[ ]
R	[ ]
A	[ ]
I	[ ]
N	[ ]

4.
G	[ ]
R	[ ]
I	[ ]
N	[ ]
D	[ ]

5.
B	[ ]
L	[ ]
E	[ ]
N	[ ]
D	[ ]

6.
C	[ ]
R	[ ]
E	[ ]
A	[ ]
M	[ ]

7.
B	[ ]
R	[ ]
A	[ ]
N	[ ]
D	[ ]

8.
E	[ ]
V	[ ]
E	[ ]
N	[ ]
T	[ ]

9.
F	[ ]
A	[ ]
R	[ ]
C	[ ]
E	[ ]

10.
W	[ ]
R	[ ]
I	[ ]
N	[ ]
G	[ ]

11.
T	[ ]
R	[ ]
A	[ ]
M	[ ]
P	[ ]

12.
S	[ ]
C	[ ]
E	[ ]
N	[ ]
T	[ ]

K

Ex.
25	[ ]
15	[ ]
24	[ ]
30	[■]
10	[ ]

1.
24	[ ]
28	[ ]
26	[ ]
32	[ ]
36	[ ]

2.
21	[ ]
29	[ ]
29	[ ]
31	[ ]
33	[ ]

3.
48	[ ]
50	[ ]
49	[ ]
47	[ ]
52	[ ]

4.
36	[ ]
32	[ ]
40	[ ]
46	[ ]
28	[ ]

5.
36	[ ]
32	[ ]
40	[ ]
46	[ ]
28	[ ]

6.
20	[ ]
23	[ ]
21	[ ]
25	[ ]
24	[ ]

Multiple Choice Answer Sheets

K

7.
95	[ ]
25	[ ]
50	[ ]
94	[ ]
70	[ ]

8.
8	[ ]
7	[ ]
13	[ ]
6	[ ]
9	[ ]

9.
70	[ ]
72	[ ]
45	[ ]
36	[ ]
48	[ ]

10.
25	[ ]
17	[ ]
30	[ ]
44	[ ]
28	[ ]

11.
16	[ ]
24	[ ]
28	[ ]
34	[ ]
30	[ ]

12.
44	[ ]
66	[ ]
54	[ ]
62	[ ]
58	[ ]

L

Ex.
GH	[ ]
EG	[ ]
EF	[ ]
FG	[■]
GF	[ ]

1.
TV	[ ]
VT	[ ]
UT	[ ]
UV	[ ]
US	[ ]

2.
RV	[ ]
SU	[ ]
ST	[ ]
PT	[ ]
SV	[ ]

3.
WX	[ ]
WZ	[ ]
XA	[ ]
AB	[ ]
WA	[ ]

4.
RL	[ ]
TM	[ ]
RM	[ ]
SL	[ ]
SM	[ ]

5.
WU	[ ]
VT	[ ]
GH	[ ]
WX	[ ]
VU	[ ]

6.
AV	[ ]
AX	[ ]
BV	[ ]
BX	[ ]
BZ	[ ]

7.
DO	[ ]
EO	[ ]
EN	[ ]
DN	[ ]
EM	[ ]

8.
HI	[ ]
HP	[ ]
HO	[ ]
GP	[ ]
IP	[ ]

9.
QP	[ ]
PP	[ ]
PQ	[ ]
QQ	[ ]
OP	[ ]

10.
MP	[ ]
LO	[ ]
MQ	[ ]
MM	[ ]
LP	[ ]

11.
QM	[ ]
LM	[ ]
KM	[ ]
MQ	[ ]
LP	[ ]

12.
AA	[ ]
ZZ	[ ]
ZA	[ ]
XB	[ ]
AZ	[ ]

M

Ex.
first	[ ]	gram	[ ]
second	[■]	kilo	[ ]
third	[ ]	metre	[■]

1.
ring	[ ]	lady	[ ]
laid	[ ]	woman	[ ]
phone	[ ]	madam	[ ]

2.
twenty	[ ]	hit	[ ]
fifteen	[ ]	run	[ ]
twelve	[ ]	twenty	[ ]

3.
slip	[ ]	water	[ ]
swing	[ ]	collapse	[ ]
chute	[ ]	jump	[ ]

4.
child	[ ]	calf	[ ]
kid	[ ]	cub	[ ]
nanny	[ ]	trunk	[ ]

5.
brother	[ ]	clean	[ ]
throw	[ ]	tidy	[ ]
laugh	[ ]	cry	[ ]

6.
child	[ ]	saddle	[ ]
young	[ ]	two	[ ]
three	[ ]	ride	[ ]

7.
June	[ ]	October	[ ]
November	[ ]	December	[ ]
February	[ ]	January	[ ]

8.
heaven	[ ]	wine	[ ]
degrees	[ ]	jug	[ ]
wings	[ ]	litres	[ ]

9.
margarine	[ ]	bottle	[ ]
cup	[ ]	grapes	[ ]
milk	[ ]	squash	[ ]

10.
shop	[ ]	plant	[ ]
meat	[ ]	market	[ ]
knife	[ ]	vegetables	[ ]

11.
driver	[ ]	sky	[ ]
garage	[ ]	hangar	[ ]
van	[ ]	wings	[ ]

Multiple Choice Answer Sheets

12.

M

glasses	[ ]	sniff	[ ]
sight	[ ]	nostril	[ ]
blind	[ ]	smell	[ ]

N

1.

124461	[ ]
122468	[ ]
124468	[ ]
124486	[ ]
122486	[ ]

2.

488678	[ ]
477867	[ ]
488687	[ ]
466786	[ ]
466876	[ ]

3.

ENABLED	[ ]
BLENDED	[ ]
ENDORSE	[ ]
LADDER	[ ]
BOBSLED	[ ]

4.

89524	[ ]
98425	[ ]
98524	[ ]
89425	[ ]
98542	[ ]

5.

51429	[ ]
51249	[ ]
15249	[ ]
15429	[ ]
15942	[ ]

6.

SMILERS	[ ]
SLALOMS	[ ]
TALLEST	[ ]
SMALLEST	[ ]
STEAMER	[ ]

7.

123349	[ ]
124469	[ ]
126649	[ ]
124496	[ ]
126694	[ ]

8.

429686	[ ]
429858	[ ]
492686	[ ]
492685	[ ]
429585	[ ]

9.

STEAL	[ ]
TEASE	[ ]
STATE	[ ]
TASTE	[ ]
STAGE	[ ]

10.

9189652	[ ]
9189265	[ ]
9182695	[ ]
9182965	[ ]
9189562	[ ]

11.

158866	[ ]
195688	[ ]
159688	[ ]
159866	[ ]
195866	[ ]

12

CLASS	[ ]
CLEAR	[ ]
CAKES	[ ]
CLEAN	[ ]
CLIMB	[ ]

13.

87645	[ ]
86745	[ ]
86754	[ ]
87547	[ ]
76845	[ ]

14.

76483	[ ]
76843	[ ]
67483	[ ]
67543	[ ]
76583	[ ]

15.

PLASMA	[ ]
STEALS	[ ]
STEAMS	[ ]
STAPLE	[ ]
LATEST	[ ]

16.

6917497	[ ]
6919749	[ ]
6194794	[ ]
6197494	[ ]
6914794	[ ]

17.

61436	[ ]
16436	[ ]
61346	[ ]
61436	[ ]
16316	[ ]

18.

DEMISE	[ ]
DEVICE	[ ]
DIVIDE	[ ]
DIVINE	[ ]
DESIGN	[ ]

O

Ex.

ripe	[ ]
pier	[ ]
pipe	[■]
peep	[ ]
pine	[ ]

1.

fact	[ ]
coat	[ ]
fort	[ ]
cart	[ ]
coal	[ ]

2.

toes	[ ]
sent	[ ]
note	[ ]
tens	[ ]
tone	[ ]

3.

lead	[ ]
wade	[ ]
weld	[ ]
deal	[ ]
dale	[ ]

4.

crate	[ ]
cater	[ ]
caret	[ ]
track	[ ]
trace	[ ]

Multiple Choice Answer Sheets

O

5.
teak	[ ]
stab	[ ]
task	[ ]
seat	[ ]
seas	[ ]

6.
find	[ ]
dine	[ ]
fine	[ ]
fend	[ ]
diet	[ ]

7.
cables	[ ]
fables	[ ]
sables	[ ]
gables	[ ]
tables	[ ]

8.
let	[ ]
set	[ ]
see	[ ]
lee	[ ]
tee	[ ]

9.
pair	[ ]
lair	[ ]
rail	[ ]
pail	[ ]
laps	[ ]

10.
tars	[ ]
arts	[ ]
star	[ ]
stir	[ ]
tart	[ ]

11.
fight	[ ]
sight	[ ]
night	[ ]
might	[ ]
right	[ ]

12.
sore	[ ]
sort	[ ]
toes	[ ]
rose	[ ]
soak	[ ]

P

Ex.
20	[ ]
25	[ ]
40	[ ]
30	[■]
35	[ ]

1.
41	[ ]
47	[ ]
49	[ ]
46	[ ]
43	[ ]

2.
47	[ ]
41	[ ]
46	[ ]
49	[ ]
43	[ ]

3.
32	[ ]
31	[ ]
36	[ ]
29	[ ]
33	[ ]

4.
21	[ ]
23	[ ]
19	[ ]
20	[ ]
22	[ ]

5.
22	[ ]
21	[ ]
23	[ ]
19	[ ]
20	[ ]

6.
10	[ ]
8	[ ]
3	[ ]
2	[ ]
5	[ ]

7.
10	[ ]
6	[ ]
9	[ ]
7	[ ]
8	[ ]

8.
72	[ ]
48	[ ]
40	[ ]
42	[ ]
38	[ ]

9.
16	[ ]
18	[ ]
15	[ ]
13	[ ]
11	[ ]

10.
9	[ ]
12	[ ]
7	[ ]
13	[ ]
8	[ ]

11.
48	[ ]
72	[ ]
144	[ ]
120	[ ]
96	[ ]

12.
37	[ ]
45	[ ]
47	[ ]
38	[ ]
40	[ ]

Q

Ex.
motor	[■]	engine	[ ]
gas	[ ]	bus	[ ]
electric	[ ]	cycle	[■]

1.
body	[ ]	your	[ ]
arm	[ ]	their	[ ]
leg	[ ]	our	[ ]

2.
all	[ ]	sow	[ ]
many	[ ]	owed	[ ]
none	[ ]	owned	[ ]

3.
stump	[ ]	alive	[ ]
stub	[ ]	create	[ ]
bust	[ ]	born	[ ]

4.
real	[ ]	ill	[ ]
dirt	[ ]	sent	[ ]
mess	[ ]	age	[ ]

5.
heat	[ ]	him	[ ]
sun	[ ]	her	[ ]
shine	[ ]	there	[ ]

6.
swallow	[ ]	up	[ ]
sup	[ ]	port	[ ]
sip	[ ]	poise	[ ]

7.
be	[ ]	shore	[ ]
see	[ ]	view	[ ]
fee	[ ]	long	[ ]

8.
half	[ ]	many	[ ]
whole	[ ]	some	[ ]
part	[ ]	all	[ ]

Multiple Choice Answer Sheets

9.

Q

trod	[ ]	den	[ ]
walked	[ ]	hole	[ ]
guard	[ ]	in	[ ]

10.

out	[ ]	peck	[ ]
on	[ ]	sure	[ ]
in	[ ]	time	[ ]

11.

made	[ ]	bring	[ ]
occur	[ ]	red	[ ]
blind	[ ]	grey	[ ]

12.

pound	[ ]	rally	[ ]
dollar	[ ]	race	[ ]
cent	[ ]	run	[ ]

Ex.

R

prove	[ ]
drove	[■]
roped	[ ]
rover	[ ]
prone	[ ]

1.

fund	[ ]
bend	[ ]
fuss	[ ]
fend	[ ]
send	[ ]

2.

corns	[ ]
snare	[ ]
cover	[ ]
score	[ ]
snore	[ ]

3.

plate	[ ]
plant	[ ]
plane	[ ]
pedal	[ ]
paled	[ ]

4.

locate	[ ]
ember	[ ]
tramp	[ ]
amber	[ ]
treat	[ ]

5.

beast	[ ]
least	[ ]
blast	[ ]
leans	[ ]
lines	[ ]

6.

trace	[ ]
caned	[ ]
fiend	[ ]
trend	[ ]
trice	[ ]

7.

baste	[ ]
taste	[ ]
trade	[ ]
tasty	[ ]
trams	[ ]

8.

dirty	[ ]
diver	[ ]
dried	[ ]
dived	[ ]
debit	[ ]

9.

lean	[ ]
lace	[ ]
line	[ ]
lane	[ ]
lice	[ ]

10.

slant	[ ]
brand	[ ]
stead	[ ]
steal	[ ]
stand	[ ]

11.

claim	[ ]
clear	[ ]
cream	[ ]
realm	[ ]
crime	[ ]

Ex.

S

OFFICE	[ ]
CHAIN	[ ]
BEACH	[ ]
FARM	[ ]
STABLE	[■]

1.

MUSCLE	[ ]
TIN	[ ]
ENERGY	[ ]
MIGHT	[ ]
MAYBE	[ ]

2.

NOTICE	[ ]
LOOK	[ ]
PROMOTION	[ ]
POINT	[ ]
DIRECTION	[ ]

3.

STREAM	[ ]
END	[ ]
DRIP	[ ]
LOWER	[ ]
DROP	[ ]

4.

NICE	[ ]
HAPPY	[ ]
CLUB	[ ]
KIND	[ ]
BAND	[ ]

Multiple Choice Answer Sheets

S

5.

HEARTY	[ ]
WELL	[ ]
JUMP	[ ]
TAP	[ ]
SPRITE	[ ]

6.

FLAP	[ ]
SIGN	[ ]
CREASE	[ ]
WHISPER	[ ]
SEA	[ ]

7.

VICTORIOUS	[ ]
SMACKED	[ ]
SLAPPED	[ ]
LOST	[ ]
BEATEN	[ ]

8.

BILL	[ ]
HURRY	[ ]
CHARGE	[ ]
PRICE	[ ]
HIT	[ ]

9.

CLING	[ ]
HOLD	[ ]
CLAW	[ ]
CATCH	[ ]
SPRING	[ ]

10.

STREAK	[ ]
FANFARE	[ ]
BAND	[ ]
CHEVRON	[ ]
UNDRESS	[ ]

11.

PREPARE	[ ]
CHARGE	[ ]
DIRECT	[ ]
RUN	[ ]
CO-ORDINATE	[ ]

12.

POINT	[ ]
AIM	[ ]
DREAM	[ ]
ASPIRATION	[ ]
LOCATION	[ ]

U

Ex.

SU	[ ]
WU	[ ]
ST	[ ]
UV	[■]
VU	[ ]

1.

AZ	[ ]
BZ	[ ]
CY	[ ]
AY	[ ]
BY	[ ]

2.

JE	[ ]
JC	[ ]
ID	[ ]
KC	[ ]
JD	[ ]

3.

NY	[ ]
NE	[ ]
PE	[ ]
QE	[ ]
PY	[ ]

4.

HV	[ ]
HU	[ ]
HW	[ ]
AW	[ ]
AU	[ ]

5.

BW	[ ]
BV	[ ]
ZV	[ ]
AW	[ ]
ZZ	[ ]

6.

NM	[ ]
MN	[ ]
LN	[ ]
LM	[ ]
ML	[ ]

7.

LL	[ ]
LM	[ ]
KL	[ ]
LK	[ ]
LJ	[ ]

8.

MV	[ ]
LU	[ ]
LV	[ ]
MU	[ ]
NV	[ ]

9.

RR	[ ]
QS	[ ]
QR	[ ]
RQ	[ ]
QQ	[ ]

10.

FE	[ ]
EF	[ ]
GE	[ ]
GF	[ ]
GE	[ ]

11.

UC	[ ]
VD	[ ]
VB	[ ]
VC	[ ]
UB	[ ]

12.

FE	[ ]
HD	[ ]
GD	[ ]
HE	[ ]
GE	[ ]

Z

1.

8.30	[ ]
8.15	[ ]
8.35	[ ]
8.45	[ ]
8.55	[ ]

2.

A	[ ]
B	[ ]
C	[ ]
D	[ ]
E	[ ]

3.

12	[ ]
11	[ ]
8	[ ]
14	[ ]
10	[ ]

4.

6	[ ]
9	[ ]
5	[ ]
8	[ ]
7	[ ]

5.

Eleanor	[ ]
Matthew	[ ]
Callum	[ ]
Duncan	[ ]
Emma	[ ]

6.

Tuesday	[ ]
Thursday	[ ]
Friday	[ ]
Monday	[ ]
Sunday	[ ]

7

Giles	[ ]
Bobby	[ ]
Habib	[ ]
Melanie	[ ]
Isabella	[ ]

8.

Christopher	[ ]
Gemma	[ ]
Owen	[ ]
Carol	[ ]
William	[ ]

Answers

	A	B	C	D	E
1	F	waist / decline	DIVER	brief / short	electric eels
2	T	engross / exist	LRKYCO	disperse / scatter	enormous items
3	K	twist / jump	EXAMPLE	interior / inside	sergeant ripped
4	N	priest / church	DKFPAD	loathe / hate	fires ignite
5	P	uncertain / unwell	DANCE	odour / smell	always eats
6	D	artistic / musical	MHUWFU	penetrate / pierce	miss our
7	M	tears / sniff	CLIMB	prohibited / forbidden	cocoa taste
8	K	height / weight	KOSOXN	reluctant / unwilling	local farmers
9	A	pencil / paper	THERE	deliberately / purposely	paste poured
10	S	radio / telephone	RRFRZ	eventually / finally	plan everything
11	W	socks / tights	JUMPER	ordinarily / normally	home at
12	R	aluminium / iron	IQQTPC	abrupt / sudden	Both atlases

	F	G	H	I	J	K
1	ATE	C	minority / majority	19	TIRED / SPIRES (R)	36
2	NOT	B	failure / success	7	PACE / BLOND (L)	31
3	ALL	D	foolish / wise	10	RAIN / FIBRE (B)	50
4	TEN	B	advance / retreat	13	RIND / BEGAN (G)	32
5	TOO	E	arrival / departure	32	BEND / CLAMP (L)	36
6	END	C	bold / timid	26	CRAM / CHEAT (E)	20
7	PEN	D	conceal / reveal	6	BRAN / MEDAL (D)	50
8	ARM	A	danger / safety	12	EVEN / LITRE (T)	9
9	WHO	E	tranquil / rough	23	FARE / PATCH (C)	72
10	EVE	D	innocent / guilty	6	RING / SWELL (W)	25
11	HIS	C	permit / forbid	0	TRAM / REPLY (P)	34
12	RAN	A	plentiful / scarce	16	CENT / PURSE (S)	54

	L	M	N		N (continued)
1	VT	laid / madam	124468	13	86745
2	RV	twelve / twenty	466876	14	76483
3	WA	slip / collapse	ENABLED	15	STAPLE
4	RL	kid / calf	89425	16	6914794
5	VU	laugh / cry	15249	17	61346
6	AV	three / two	SMALLEST	18	DEVICE
7	DN	February / October	124469		
8	HO	degrees / litres	429585		
9	QQ	milk / grapes	TASTE		
10	LO	meat / vegetables	9189265		
11	MQ	garage / hangar	159866		
12	ZZ	sight / smell	CLEAR		

Answers

	O	P	Q	R	S	U	Z
1	coat	49	arm our	fend	MIGHT	AZ	8.15
2	tone	43	all owed	snore	NOTICE	ID	B
3	wade	32	stub born	plate	DROP	PY	10
4	trace	22	mess age	treat	KIND	HV	8
5	task	22	heat her	least	WELL	AW	Eleanor
6	find	5	sup port	trend	FLAP	LM	Thursday
7	tables	10	be long	trade	BEATEN	KL	Giles, Habib
8	let	38	whole some	dirty	CHARGE	LU	Gemma
9	lair	18	trod den	lane	CATCH	QQ	
10	star	12	in sure	stand	BAND	EF	
11	might	120	occur red	clear	RUN	UC	
12	sort	37	cent rally		AIM	GD	